Father Damien

AN OPEN LETTER TO THE

REVEREND DOCTOR HYDE

OF HONOLULU

Damien de Veuster

Father Damien

AN

OPEN LETTER

TO THE

Reverend Doctor Hyde

OF HONOLULU

FROM

Robert Louis Stevenson

Foreword by George L. McKay

Cobble Hill Press *New York*

Library of Congress Catalog Number 67–27293
FIRST PRINTING
Manufactured in the United States of America
Distributed by Hill & Wang, Inc.

FOREWORD

JOSEPH DE VEUSTER was born on January 3, 1840, on a little farm at Tremeloo in Belgium, six miles from Louvain. He was the seventh child of a Flemish farmer, François de Veuster, and his wife Catherine. The boy's parents sent him to the college at Braine-le-Comte in the province of Hainault, where he studied French. They hoped that he would undertake a commercial career, but in 1858 Joseph announced that he wished to study for the priesthood. The parents objected at first, but after a time yielded to their son's wishes and sent him to the Convent of the Picpus

Fathers at Louvain, where his brother Augustus had already become Father Pamphile. On October 8, 1860, at the Novitiate of Issy near Paris, Joseph took the vows of poverty, chastity, and obedience as a Brother of the Sacred Hearts of Jesus and Mary. When he entered upon his noviate he was given the name Damien, after Saint Damien of Cilicia, who was beheaded about 287 A.D. In 1863 Father Pamphile was about to leave as a missionary to Hawaii. When he contracted typhus, however, and it appeared that he would not live, Joseph was permitted to go in his place.

Damien's voyage to Hawaii began in October 1863, and ended, after a severe storm at Cape Horn, at Honolulu on March 19, 1864. Two months after his arrival he was ordained as a priest on Whitsunday, 1864. From 1864 to 1873 Damien was in charge of Roman Catholic activities in various districts on the island of Hawaii. He was a devoted missionary to the natives and built several chapels with his own hands. On May 10, 1873, he offered his services as resident priest to the afflicted in the leper colony at Kalaupapa on the island of Molokai. At that time there were six hundred lepers segregated in this settlement. They were provided with food, clothing, and housing by the government but their lives were meager. Damien not only ministered to their spiritual needs but also gave them such medical services as he was able to provide, and helped them in other ways, such as building cottages. In 1885 he became a leper himself. At that time he was assisted by two other priests and two lay brothers. He died of leprosy on April 15, 1889.

In the second half of 1888 Robert

Louis Stevenson, with members of his family, visited the Marquesas, the Paumotus, and the Society Islands in the Pacific. In the first half of 1889 he was settled in Honolulu, only a short distance from the leper colony at Kalaupapa, which he visited in May 1889, the month after Damien's death. Stevenson spent a week at the settlement and found the experience harrowing. While there he learned a good deal about Father Damien, and in June he wrote to Sidney Colvin, his friend and principal literary advisor: "Of old Damien, whose weaknesses and worse perhaps I heard fully, I think only the more. It was a European peasant: dirty, bigoted, untruthful, unwise, tricky, but superb with generosity, residual candour and fundamental good-humour. . . . A man, with all the grime and paltriness of mankind, but a Saint and hero all the more for that." Stevenson left the Hawaiian Islands in the second half of June for another long cruise in the Pacific.

Another resident of Honolulu, the Rev. Dr. Charles McEwen Hyde, was, according to Dr. Arthur Albert St. M. Mouritz, "scholarly, polished and refined; he came from New England and belonged to the best class of Americans." He was a Presbyterian minister and lived in some affluence. In September 1885 he had attended the dedication of the Protestant church at Kalaupapa and made a careful examination of the schools and homes which Damien had founded for orphaned children. According to Dr. Mouritz, Dr. Hyde persuaded two wealthy men, Charles R. Bishop and Henry P. Baldwin, to found two homes at Kalawao (near the leper colony), which bear their names. There was rivalry and perhaps ill will between the Catholic and Protestant establishments at and near the leper colony.

After Father Damien's death, laudatory accounts of his achievements were published in papers in various parts of the world. It was perhaps in July that the Rev. H. B. Gage, a Methodist minister in Australia, having read one or more of these accounts, wrote to his friend, Dr. Hyde, asking the latter's opinion of Father Damien. On August 2 Hyde wrote to Gage that Damien "was a coarse, dirty man, headstrong and bigoted. . . . He had no hand in the reforms and improvements inaugurated, which were the work of our Board of Health. . . . He was not a pure man in his relations with women, and leprosy of which he died should be attributed to his vices and carelessness. . . ." (The full text of this letter is recorded on pages 23–24.) According to Stevenson's biographer J.A. Steuart, Dr. Hyde's letter "was not meant for publication, and got into print without the writer's sanction or knowledge." Among other periodicals, this letter was published in *The Presbyterian*, a weekly issued in Sydney, Australia, and in *The English Churchman* of London.

Stevenson visited the Gilbert Islands and Samoa in the second half of 1889 and arrived in Sydney in February 1890. There he was shown Dr. Hyde's letter in *The Presbyterian.* Stevenson's wrath was immediately aroused, and in a single day he composed his letter of unrestrained denunciation of Dr. Hyde. In this celebrated philippic, dated February 25, one blow of invective follows another without mercy, and all Hyde's accusations are answered with caustic replies. According to Mrs. R. L. S., Stevenson "hired a printer [in Sydney] by the day [to print the *Letter*], and the work was rushed through." The private printing (probably by W. M. MacLardy) of twenty-five copies in pamphlet form was completed on or before March 12. On that day, Stevenson wrote to Charles Baxter: "Enclosed please find a libel: you perceive I am quite frank with my legal advisor; and I will also add it is *conceivable* an action might be brought, and in that event *probable* I should be ruined. If you had been through my experience, you would understand how little I care; for upon this topic my zeal is complete and, probably enough, without discretion." R.L.S. fully expected to deal with a libel suit, but there was none. The worst reply from Dr. Hyde was apparently his remark that Stevenson was a "Bohemian crank."

Following the Sydney pamphlet, the

Open Letter appeared in *The Scots Observer*, Edinburgh, May 3 and 10, 1890; in a supplement to the *Elele*, Honolulu, May 10; and in *The Australian Star*, Sydney, on May 24 under the title *In Defense of the Dead*. A selection from the *Letter* was printed in *The Critic*, New York, May 24. Thirty copies of it were privately printed in Edinburgh by T. & A. Constable, of which some or all were distributed in June. A second issue of this edition (the first issue *published* in book form) was offered by Chatto and Windus in London on July 16. Many separate editions appeared in succeeding years, including those published by Thomas B. Mosher of Portland, Maine; by *The Cornhill Booklet* of Boston; by Howard Wilford Bell of Oxford; and by the Ave Maria Press of Notre Dame, Indiana. The *Letter* was published in 1895 in Volume XI of the Edinburgh Edition of Stevenson's writings. It was published in the same year by Charles Scribner's Sons in Volume IV of their Thistle Edition; and subsequently in the Biographical, Household, Vailima, Tusitala, Skerryvore, and South Seas Editions of Stevenson's collected writings.

In 1911 the editor of *Ave Maria* (Notre Dame, Indiana) wrote: "Feeling sure that some day 'in his resting grave' the defender of Father Damien [i.e., Stevenson] would need to be defended himself, we took care several years ago to secure from Mrs. Stevenson a statement regarding the *Open Letter to the Rev. Dr. Hyde.* In answer to our inquiry as to the truth of the assertion, so often repeated, that her husband regretted the letter, and that before his death his opinion of Father Damien had undergone a change, Mrs. Stevenson entered an indignantly emphatic denial. Mrs. Stevenson's words were: As to the *Open Letter to Dr. Hyde*, nothing can make me believe that Louis ever regretted the subject-matter of that piece of writing. To me, up to his last hour, he spoke always in the same strain. His admiration for the work and character of 'that saint, that martyr,' as he invariably called Father Damien, remained unchanged; and, any mention of the cowardly attack on the dead man's memory brought a flush of anger into his face and a fire to his eye that were unmistakable. . . ."

If this is a faithful report of the statement Mrs. Stevenson made a few years before 1911, she verified her husband's loyalty in his admiration for Father Damien, but apparently failed to disclose the fact that he regretted in any way his letter to Dr. Hyde. Possibly she never knew that six months or less after he had written it he was sorry that he had expressed his feelings in the terms which survive. In answer to a letter from Andrew Chatto about possible royalties for the Chatto and Windus issue of the *Open Letter*, Stevenson wrote him in August 1890: "The letter to Dr. Hyde is yours, or any man's. I will never touch a penny of remuneration. I do not stick at murder; I draw the line at cannibalism; I could not eat a penny roll that piece of bludgeoning had gained for me." And in September of that year Stevenson composed a letter to Mrs. Charles S. Fairchild, an American lady, in which he wrote: "I regret also my letter to Dr. Hyde. Yes, I do; I think it was barbarously harsh; if I did it now, I would defend Damien no less well, and give less pain to those who are alive. . . . On the whole, it was virtuous to defend Damien; but it was harsh to strike so hard at Dr. Hyde. . . . I have deeply wounded one of his colleagues whom I esteemed and liked."

Dr. Hyde's colleague here mentioned was probably the Rev F. Damon, a Protestant missionary in Hawaii.*

Robert Louis Stevenson's impassioned letter on Damien of Molokai is one of the most moving documents in defense of a fellow human being ever written. It will endure as long as men respect the great spiritual truths reflected in the life of Damien de Veuster.

George L. McKay

*The originals of the letters to Chatto and Mrs. Fairchild are in the Beinecke Library at Yale University.

Father Damien

AN OPEN LETTER TO THE REVEREND DOCTOR HYDE OF HONOLULU

Robert Louis Stevenson's

LETTER

Sydney
FEBRUARY 25, 1890.

SIR,

It may probably occur to you that we have met, and visited, and conversed; on my side, with interest. You may remember that you have done me several courtesies, for which I was prepared to be grateful. But there are duties which come before gratitude, and offences which justly divide friends, far more acquaintances. Your letter to the Reverend H. B. Gage is a document, which, in my sight, if you had filled me with bread when I was starving, if you had sat up to nurse my father when he lay a-dying, would yet absolve me from the bonds of gratitude. You know enough, doubtless, of the process of canonisation to be aware that, a hundred years after the death of Damien, there will appear a man charged with the painful office of the *devil's advocate*. After that noble brother of mine, and of all frail clay, shall have lain a century at rest, one shall accuse, one defend him. The circumstance is unusual that the devil's advocate should be a volunteer, should be a member of a sect immediately rival, and should make haste to take upon himself his ugly office ere the bones are cold; unusual, and of a taste which I shall leave my readers free to qualify; unusual, and to me inspiring. If I have at all learned the trade of using words to convey truth and to arouse emotion, you have at last furnished me with a subject. For it is in the interest of all mankind and the cause of public decency in every quarter of the world, not only that Damien should be righted, but that you and your letter should be displayed at length, in their true colors, to the public eye.

To do this properly, I must begin by quoting you at large: I shall then proceed to criticise your utterance from several points of view, divine and human, in the course of which I shall attempt to draw again and with more specification, the character of the dead saint whom it has pleased you to vilify: so much being done, I shall say farewell to you for ever.

LETTER OF REV. C. MCE. HYDE

Honolulu
AUGUST 2, 1889.

REV. H. B. GAGE.

Dear Brother,—In answer to your inquiries about Father Damien, I can only reply that we who knew the man are surprised at the extravagant newspaper laudations, as if he was a most saintly philanthropist. The simple truth is, he was a coarse, dirty man, headstrong and bigoted. He was not sent to Molokai, but went there without orders; did not stay at the leper settlement (before he became one himself), but circulated freely over the whole island (less than half the island is devoted to the lepers), and he came often to Honolulu. He had no hand in the reforms and improvements inaugurated, which were the work of our Board of Health, as occasion required and means provided. He was not a pure man in his relations with women, and the leprosy of which he died should be attributed to his vices and carelessness. Others have done much for the lepers, our own ministers, the government physicians, and so forth, but never with the Catholic idea of meriting eternal life.—Yours, etc.

C. M HYDE.

To deal fitly with a letter so extraordinary, I must draw at the outset on my private knowledge of the signatory and his sect. It may offend others; scarcely you, who have been so busy to collect, so bold to publish, gossip on your rivals. And this is perhaps the moment when I may best explain to you the character of what you are to read: I conceive you as a man quite beyond and below the reticences of civility: with what measure you mete, with that shall it be measured you again; with you, at last, I rejoice to feel the button off the foil and to plunge home. And if in aught that I shall say I should offend others, your colleagues, whom I respect and remember with affection, I can but offer them my regret; I am not free, I am inspired by the consideration of interests far more large; and such pain as can be inflicted by anything from me must be indeed trifling when compared with the pain with which they read your letter.

It is not the hangman, but the criminal, that brings dishonor on the house.

You belong, sir, to a sect—I believe my sect, and that in which my ancesters labored—which has enjoyed, and partly failed to utilise, an exceptional advantage in the islands of Hawaii. The first missionaries came; they found the land already self-purged of its old and bloody faith; they were embraced, almost on their arrival, with enthusiasm; what troubles they supported came far more from whites than from Hawaiians; and to these last they stood (in a rough figure) in the shoes of God. This is not the place to enter into the degree or causes of their failure, such as it is. One element alone is pertinent, and must here be plainly dealt with. In the course of their evangelical calling, they—or too many of them—grew rich. It may be news to you that the houses of missionaries are a cause of mocking on the streets of Honolulu.

It will at least be news to you, that when I returned your civil visit, the driver of my cab commented on the size, the taste, and the comfort of your home. It would have been news certainly to myself, had any one told me that afternoon that I should live to drag such matter into print. But you see, sir, how you degrade better men to your own level; and it is needful that those who are to judge betwixt you and me, betwixt Damien and the devil's advocate, should understand your letter to have been penned in a house which could raise, and that very justly, the envy and comments of the passers-by. I think (to employ a phrase of yours which I admire) it "should be attributed" to you that you have never visited the scene of Damien's life and death. If you had, and had recalled it, and looked about your pleasant rooms, even your pen perhaps would have been stayed.

Your sect (and remember, as far as

any sect avows me, it is mine) has not done ill in a worldly sense in the Hawaiian Kingdom. When calamity befell their innocent parishioners, when leprosy descended and took root in the Eight Islands, a *quid pro quo* was to be looked for. To that prosperous mission, and to you as one of its adornments, God had sent at last an opportunity. I know I am touching here upon a nerve acutely sensitive. I know that others of your colleagues look back on the inertia of your church, and the intrusive and decisive heroism of Damien, with something almost to be called remorse. I am sure it is so with yourself; I am persuaded your letter was inspired by a certain envy, not essentially ignoble, and the one human trait to be espied in that performance. You were thinking of the lost chance, the past day; of that which should have been conceived and was not; of the service due and not rendered. *Time was*, said the voice in your ear, in your pleasant room, as you sat raging and writing; and if the words written were base beyond parallel, the rage, I am happy to repeat—it is the only compliment I shall pay you—the rage was almost virtuous. But, sir, when we have failed, and another has succeeded; when we have stood by, and another has stepped in; when we sit and grow bulky in our charming mansions, and a plain, uncouth peasant steps into the battle, under the eyes of God, and succours the afflicted, and consoles the dying, and is himself afflicted in his turn, and dies upon the field of honor—the battle cannot be retrieved as your unhappy irritation has suggested. It is a lost battle, and lost for ever. One thing remained to you in your defeat—some rags of common honor; and these you have made haste to cast away.

Common honor; not the honor of

having done anything right, but the honor of not having done aught conspicuously foul; the honor of the inert: that was what remained to you. We are not all expected to be Damiens; a man may conceive his duty more narrowly, he may love his comforts better; and none will cast a stone at him for that. But will a gentleman of your reverend profession allow me an example from the fields of gallantry? When two gentlemen compete for the favor of a lady, and the one succeeds and the other is rejected, and (as will sometimes happen) matter damaging to the successful rival's credit reaches the ear of the defeated, it is held by plain men of no pretensions that his mouth is, in the circumstance, almost necessarily closed. Your church and Damien's were in Hawaii upon a rivalry to do well: to help, to edify, to set divine examples. You have (in one huge instance) failed, and Damien succeeded. I marvel it should not have occurred to you that you were doomed to silence; that when you had been outstripped in that high rivalry, and sat inglorious in the midst of your well-being, in your pleasant room—and Damien, crowned with glories and horrors, toiled and rotted in that pig-sty of his under the cliffs of Kalawao—you, the elect who would not, were the last man on earth to collect and propagate gossip on the volunteer who would and did.

I think I see you—for I try to see you in the flesh as I write these sentences—I think I see you leap at the word pig-sty, a hyperbolical expression at the best. "He had no hand in the reforms," he was "a coarse, dirty man"; these were your own words; and you may think it possible that I am come to support you with fresh evidence. In a sense, it is even so. Damien has been too much depicted with a conventional halo and conventional features; so drawn by men who perhaps had not the eye to remark or the pen to express the individual; or who perhaps were only blinded and silenced by generous admiration, such as I partly envy for myself—such as you, if your soul were enlightened, would envy on your bended knees. It is the least defect of such a method of portraiture that it makes the path easy for the devil's advocate, and leaves for the misuse of the slanderer a considerable field of truth. For the truth that is suppressed by friends is the readiest weapon of the enemy. The world, in your despite, may perhaps owe you something, if your letter be the means of substituting once for all a credible likeness for a wax abstraction. For, if that world at all remember you, on the day when Damien of Molokai shall be named Saint, it will be in virtue of one work: your letter to the Reverend H. B. Gage.

You may ask on what authority I speak. It was my inclement destiny to become acquainted, not with Damien, but with Dr. Hyde. When I visited the lazaretto Damien was already in his resting grave. But such information as I have, I gathered on the spot in conversation with those who knew him well and long; some indeed who revered his memory; *but others who had sparred and wrangled with him*, who beheld him with no halo, who perhaps regarded him with *small respect*, and through whose unprepared and scarcely partial communications the plain, human features of the man shone on me convincingly. These gave me what knowledge I possess; and I learnt it in that scene where it could be most completely and sensitively understood—Kalawao, which you have never visited, about which you have never so much as endeavored to inform yourself: for, brief as your letter is, you have found the means to stumble into that confession. "*Less than one-half* of the island," you say, "is devoted to the lepers." Molokai—"*Molokai ahina,*" the "grey," lofty and most desolate island —along all its northern side plunges a front of precipice into a sea of unusual profundity. This range of cliff is, from east to west, the true end and frontier of the island. Only in one spot there projects into the ocean a certain triangular and rugged down, grassy, stony, windy, and rising in the midst into a hill with a dead crater: the whole bearing to the cliff that overhangs it somewhat the same relation as a bracket to a wall. With this hint you will now be able to pick out the leper station on a map; you will be able to judge how much of Molokai is thus cut off between the surf and precipice, whether less than a half, or less than a quarter, or a fifth, or a tenth—or say, a twentieth; and the next time you burst into print you will be in a position to share with us the issue of your calculations.

I imagine you to be one of those persons who talk with cheerfulness of that place which oxen and wainropes could not drag you to behold. You, who do not even know its situation on the map, probably denounce sensational descriptions, stretching your limbs the while in your pleasant parlor on Beretania Street. When I was pulled ashore there one early morning, there sat with me in the boat two Sisters, bidding farewell (in humble imitation of Damien) to the lights and joys of human life. One of these wept silently; I could not withhold myself from joining her. Had you been there, it is my belief that nature would have triumphed even in you; and as the boat drew but a little nearer, and you beheld the stairs crowded with abominable deformations of our common manhood, and saw yourself landing in the midst of such a population as only now and then surrounds us in the horror of a nightmare—what a haggard eye you would have rolled over your reluctant shoulder towards the house on Beretania Street! Had you gone on; had you found every fourth face a blot upon the landscape; had you visited the hospital and seen the butt-ends of human beings lying there almost unrecognisable, but still breathing, still thinking, still remembering; you would have understood that life in the lazaretto is an ordeal from which the nerves of a man's spirit shrink, even as his eye quails under the brightness of the sun; you would have felt it was (even today) a pitiful place to visit and a hell to dwell in. It is not the fear of possible infection. That seems a little thing when compared with the pain, the pity, and the disgust of the visitor's surroundings, and the atmosphere of affliction, disease, and physical disgrace in which he breathes. I do not think I am a man more than usually timid; but I never recall the days and nights I spent upon that island promontory (eight days and seven nights) without heartfelt thankfulness that I am somewhere else. I find in my diary that I speak of my stay as a "grinding experience": I have once jotted in the margin, "*Harrowing* is the word"; and when the Molokii bore me at last towards the outer world, I kept repeating to myself, with a new conception of their pregnancy, those simple words of the song—

" 'Tis the most distressful country that ever yet was seen." And observe: that which I saw and suffered from was a settlement purged, bettered, beautified; the new village built, the hospital and the Bishop Home excellently arranged; the Sisters, the doctor and the missionaries, all indefatigable in their noble tasks. It was a different place when Damien came there, and made his great renunciation, and slept that first night under a tree amidst his rotting brethren: alone with pestilence; and looking forward (with what courage, with what pitiful sinkings of dread, God only knows) to a lifetime of dressing sores and stumps.

You will say, perhaps, I am too sensitive, that sights as painful abound in cancer hospitals and are confronted daily by doctors and nurses. I have long learned to admire and envy the doctors and nurses. But there is no cancer hospital so large and populous as Kalawao and Kalaupapa; and in such a matter every fresh case, like every inch of length in the pipe of an organ, deepens the note of the impression; for what daunts the onlooker is that monstrous sum of human suffering by which he stands surrounded. Lastly, no doctor or nurse is called upon to enter once for all the doors of that gehenna; they do not say farewell, they need not abandon hope, on its sad threshold; they but go for a time to their high calling, and can look forward as they go to relief, to recreation, and to rest. But Damien shut to with his own hand the doors of his own sepulchre.

I shall now extract three passages from my dairy at Kalawao.

A. "Damien is dead and already somewhat ungratefully remembered in the field of his labors and sufferings. 'He was a good man, but very officious,' says one. Another tells me he had fallen (as other priests so easily do) into something of the ways and habits of thought of a Kanaka: but he had the wit to recognise the fact, and the good sense to laugh [over] it. A plain man it seems he was; I cannot find he was a popular."

B. "After Ragsdale's death [Ragsdale was a famous Luna, or overseer, of the unruly settlement] there followed a brief term of office by Father Damien which served only to publish the weakness of that noble man. He was rough in his ways, and he had no control. Authority was relaxed; Damien's life was threatened, and he was soon eager to resign."

C. "Of Damien," I begin to have an idea. He seems to have been a man of the peasant class, certainly of the peasant type: shrewd; ignorant and bigoted, yet with an open mind and capable of receiving and digesting a reproof if it were bluntly administered; superbly generous in the least thing as well as in the greatest, and as ready to give his last shirt (although not without human grumbling) as he had been to sacrifice his life; essentially indiscreet and officious, which made him a troublesome colleague; domineering in all his ways, which made him incurably unpopular with the Kanakas, but yet destitute of real authority, so that his boys laughed at him and he must carry out his wishes by the means of bribes. He learned to have a mania for doctoring; and set up the Kanakas against the remedies of his regular rivals; perhaps (if anything matter at all in the treatment of such a disease) the worst thing that he did, and certainly the easiest. The best and worst of the man appear very plainly in his dealings with Mr. Chapman's money; he had originally laid it out [intended to lay it out] entirely for the benefit of Catholics, and even so not wisely, but after a long, plain talk, he admitted his error fully and revised the list. The sad state of the boys' home is in part the result of his lack of control; in part, of his own slovenly ways and false ideas of hygiene. Brother officials used to call it 'Damien's Chinatown.' 'Well,' they would say, 'your Chinatown keeps growing.' And he would laugh with perfect good nature, and adhere to his errors with perfect obstinacy. So much I have gathered of truth about this plain, noble human brother and father of ours; his imperfections are the traits of his face, by which we know him for our fellow; his martyrdom and his example nothing can lessen or annul; and only a person here on the spot can properly appreciate their greatness."

I have set down these private passages, as you perceive, without correction; thanks to you, the public has them in their bluntness. They are almost a list of the man's faults, for it is rather these I was seeking: with his virtues, with the heroic profile of his life, I and the world were already sufficiently acquainted. I was besides a little suspicious of Catholic testimony: in no ill sense, but merely because Damien's admirers and disciples were the least likely to be critical. I know you will be more suspicious still; and the facts set down above were one and all collected from the lips of Protestants who had opposed the father in his life. Yet I am strangely deceived, or they build up the image of a man, with all his weaknesses, essentially heroic, and alive with rugged honesty, generosity and mirth.

Take it for what it is, rough private jottings of the worst sides of Damien's character, collected from the lips of those who had labored with and (in your own phrase) "knew the man"—though I question whether Damien would have said that he knew you. Take it, and observe with wonder how well you were served by your gossips, how ill by your intelligence and sympathy; in how many points of fact we are at one, and how widely our appreciations vary. There is something wrong here; either with you or me. It is possible, for instance, that you, who seem to have so many ears in Kalawao, had heard of the affair of Mr. Chapman's money, and were singly struck by Damien's intended wrong-doing. I was struck with that also, and set it fairly down; but I was struck much more by the fact that he had the honesty of mind to be convinced. I may here tell you that it was a long business; that one of his colleagues sat with him late into the night, multiplying arguments and accusations; that the father listened as usual with "perfect good-nature and perfect obstinacy"; but at the last, when he was persuaded—"Yes," said he, "I am very much obliged to you; you have done me a service; it would have been a theft." There are many (not Catholics merely) who require their heroes and saints to be infallible; to these the story will be painful; not to the true lovers, patrons, and servants of mankind.

And I take it, this is a type of our division; that you are one of those who have an eye for faults and failures; that you take a pleasure to find and publish them; and that, having found them, you make haste to forget the overvailing virtues and the real success which had alone introduced them to your knowledge. It is a dangerous frame of mind. That you may understand how dangerous, and into what a situation it has already brought you, we will (if you please) go hand-in-hand through the different phrases of your letter, and candidly examine each from the point of view of its truth, its appositeness, and its charity.

Damien was *coarse*.

It is very possible. You make us sorry for the lepers who had only a coarse old peasant for their friend and father. But you, who were so refined, why were you not there, to cheer them with the lights of culture? Or may I remind you that we have some reason to doubt if John the Baptist were genteel; and in the case of Peter, on whose career you doubtless dwell approvingly in the pulpit, no doubt at all he was a "coarse, headstrong" fisherman. Yet even in our Protestant Bibles Peter is called Saint.

Damien was *dirty*.

He was. Think of the poor lepers annoyed with this dirty comrade! But the clean Dr. Hyde was at his food in a fine house.

Damien was *headstrong*.

I believe you are right again; and I thank God for his strong head and heart.

Damien was *bigoted*.

I am not fond of bigots myself, because they are not fond of me. But what is meant by bigotry, that we should regard it as a blemish in a priest? Damien believed his own religion with the simplicity of a peasant or a child; as I would I could suppose that you do. For this, I wonder at him some way off; and had that been his only character, should have avoided him in life. But the point of interest in Damien, which has caused him to be so much talked about and made him at last the subject of your pen and mine, was that, in him, his bigotry, his intense and narrow faith, wrought potently for good, and strengthened him to be one of the world's heroes and examplars.

Damien *was not sent to Molokai, but went there without orders.*

Is this a misreading? or do you really mean the words for blame? I have heard Christ, in the pulpits of our church, held up for imitation, on the ground that His sacrifice was voluntary. Does Dr. Hyde think otherwise?

Damien *did not stay at the settlement, etc.*

It is true he was allowed many indulgences. Am I to understand that you blame the father for profiting by these, or the officers for granting them? In either case, it is a mighty Spartan standard to issue from the house on Beretania Street; and I am convinced you will find yourself with few supporters.

Damien *had no hand in the reforms, etc.*

I think even you will admit that I have already been frank in my description of the man I am defending; but before I take you up upon this head, I will be franker still, and tell you that perhaps nowhere in the world can a man taste a more pleasurable sense of contrast than when he passes from Damien's "Chinatown" at Kalawao to the beautiful Bishop Home at Kalaupapa. At this point, in my desire to make all fair for you, I will break my rule and adduce Catholic testimony. Here is a passage from my dairy about my visit to the "Chinatown," from which you will see how it is (even now) regarded by its own officials: "We went round all the dormitories, refectories, etc.—dark and dingy enough, with a superficial cleanliness, which he [Mr. Dutton, the lay brother] did not seek to defend. 'It is almost decent,' said he; 'the sisters will make that all right when we get them here.' " And yet I gathered it was already better since Damien was dead, and far better than when he was there alone and had his own (not always excellent) way. I have now come far enough to meet you on a common ground of fact; and I tell you that, to a mind not prejudiced by jealousy, all the reforms of the lazaretto, and even those which he most vigorously opposed, are properly the work of Damien. They are the evidence of his success; they are what his heroism provoked from the reluctant and the careless. Many were before him in the field; Mr. Meyer, for instance, of whose faithful work we hear too little: there have been many since; and some had more worldly wisdom, though none had more devotion, than our saint. Before his day, even you will confess, they had effected little. It was his part, by one striking act of martyrdom, to direct all men's eyes on that distressful country. At a blow, and with the price of his life, he made the place illustrious and public. And that, if you will consider largely, was the one reform needful; pregnant of all that should succeed. It brought money; it brought (best individual addition of them all) the sisters; it brought supervision, for public opinion and public interest landed with the man at Kalawao. If ever any man brought reforms, and died to bring them, it was he. There is not a clean cup or towel in the Bishop Home, but dirty Damien washed it.

Damien *was not a pure man in his relations with women, etc.* How do you know that? Is this the nature of the conversation in that house on Beretania Street which the cabman envied, driving past?—Racy details of the misconduct of the poor peasant priest, toiling under the cliffs of Molokai?

Many have visited the station before me; they seem not to have heard the rumor. When I was there I heard many shocking tales, for my informants were men speaking with the plainness of the laity; and I heard plenty of complaints of Damien. Why was this never mentioned? and how came it to you in the retirement of your clerical parlor?

But I must not even seem to deceive you. This scandal, when I read it in your letter, was not new to me. I had heard it once before; and I must tell you how. There came to Samoa a man from Honolulu; he, in a public-house on the beach, volunteered the statement that Damien had "contracted the disease from having connection with the female lepers"; and I find a joy in telling you how the report was welcomed in a public-house. A man sprang to his feet; I am not at liberty to give his name, but from what I heard I doubt if you would care to have him to dinner in Beretania Street. "You miserable little ——" (here is a word I dare not print, it would so shock your ears). "You miserable little ——," he cried, "if the story were a thousand times true, can't you see you are a million times a lower —— for daring to repeat it?" I wish it could be told of you that when the report reached you in your house, perhaps after family worship, you had found in your soul enough holy anger to receive it with the same expression: ay, even with that one which I dare not print; it would not need to have been blotted away, like Uncle Toby's oath, by the tears of the recording angel; it would have been counted to you for your brightest righteousness. But you have deliberately chosen the part of the man from Honolulu, and you have played it with improvements of your own. The man from Honolulu—miserable, leering creature—communicated the tale to a rude knot of beach-combing drinkers in a public-house, where (I will so far agree with your temperance opinions) man is not always at his noblest; and the man from Honolulu had himself been drinking—drinking, we may charitably fancy, to excess. It was to your "dear Brother, the Reverend H. B. Gage," that you chose to communicate the sickening story; and the blue ribbon which adorns your portly bosom forbids me to allow you the extenuating plea that you were drunk when by you it was done. Your "dear brother"—a brother indeed—made haste to deliver up your letter (as a means of grace, perhaps) to the religious papers; where, after many months, I have found and read and wondered at it; and whence I have now reproduced it for the wonder of others. And you and your dear brother have, by this cycle of operations, built up a contrast very edifying to examine in detail. The man whom you would not care to have to dinner, on the one side; on the other, the Reverend Dr. Hyde and the Reverend H. B. Gage: the Apia bar-room, the Honolulu manse.

But I fear you scarce appreciate how you appear to your fellow-men; and to bring it home to you, I will suppose your story to be true. I will suppose—and God forgive me for supposing it—that Damien faltered and stumbled in his narrow path of duty; I will suppose that, in the horror of his isolation, perhaps in the fever of incipient disease, he, who was doing so much more than he had sworn, failed in the letter of his priestly oath—he, who was so much a better man than either you or me, who did what we have never dreamed of daring—he too tasted of our common frailty. "O, Iago, the pity of it!" The least tender should be moved to tears; the most incredulous to prayer. And all that you could do was to pen your letter to the Reverend H. B. Gage!

Is it growing at all clear to you what a picture you have drawn of your own heart? I will try yet once again to make it clearer. You had a father: suppose this tale were about him, and some informant brought it to you, proof in hand: I am not making too high an estimate of your emotional nature when I suppose you would regret the circumstance? that you would feel the tale of frailty the more keenly since it shamed the author of your days? and that the last thing you would do would be to publish it in the religious press? Well, the man who tried to do what Damien did, is my father, and the father of the man in the Apia bar, and the father of all who love goodness; and he was your father too, if God had given you grace to see it.

ROBERT LOUIS STEVENSON

The text of this book is set in
Linotype Monticello
by V & M Typographical, Inc.
Printed by Halliday Lithograph Corp.
and bound by The Book Press.
Typography and binding design by
VINCENT TORRE